William Shakespeare

Hamlet

Retold by
Marcia Williams

WALKER
BOOKS

William Shakespeare

Hamlet

First published 2015 by Walker Books Ltd
87 Vauxhall Walk, London SE11 5HJ

2 4 6 8 10 9 7 5 3 1

This book has been typeset in Kennerly Regular

Printed and bound in Germany

British Library Cataloguing in Publication Data:
a catalogue record for this book is available from the British Library

ISBN 978-1-4063-6269-5

www.walker.co.uk

For Sophie

Contents

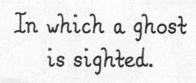

In which a ghost
is sighted.

Long ago in Denmark, the ghost of a man
was seen to walk the high, bleak, windswept
battlements of Elsinore Castle. He uttered
not a word and his footsteps made no sound
against the crashing of the surf on the cliffs
below. Twice now, the night guards had
reported seeing the ghostly figure walk
silently along the battlements. He was
dressed in full armour and a long cloak

whipped the wind behind him. The guards were certain he was not a figment of their imagination. Indeed, they believed he was the spirit of their late king.

The king had been dead for two months and good sense told the guards that his spirit would not return to haunt them, yet they could not shake the idea. Brave as they were, the night soldiers trembled with fear at the unnatural sight. The phantom looked so sad and troubled, but he would not speak, even when a watchman cried out, "What art thou? By heaven, I charge thee, speak!"

Hamlet, Prince of Denmark, son of the late king and heir to his crown, had idolized his father and was completely devastated by his sudden death. His father had been bitten by a serpent while sleeping in his orchard, so his death was unexpected and untimely. The old king had been a great monarch, loved and honoured by all the people of Denmark. Hamlet had thought his mother, Queen Gertrude, also loved his father, but now he wondered. For while the old king's grave was still freshly dug, she had cast off her widow's garments and married her husband's brother, Claudius, making him the new king. Hamlet hated his mother for

feasting and flirting when the meats from his father's funeral were hardly cooled – and he was not the only one to be outraged. Many felt that Queen Gertrude had not shown proper respect to their beloved king.

Hamlet did not mind his uncle stealing his crown, for he was not a youth eager for power, but he thought his uncle was unworthy to rule Denmark. Poor Hamlet – all his old love of life and learning had vanished. His mood grew blacker by the day and he could hardly bring himself to speak to his mother, or her husband, King Claudius.

In which Hamlet is given a terrible task.

When Hamlet's friend Horatio told him that his father's ghost, dressed in full armour, had been seen on the battlements, Hamlet listened with foreboding. It seemed to confirm his worst fears. "My father's spirit in arms! All is not well," he muttered.

That night, Hamlet stood watch with Horatio and the guards, hoping and yet dreading to see his father's spirit. The air bit

shrewdly at the watchers, even though they
were wrapped in thick cloaks. Then, as the
hour neared midnight, the ghost appeared
as if from nowhere. Silently, he beckoned to
Hamlet. Horatio tried to stop Hamlet from
following the ghost, begging, "Do not, my
lord." But Hamlet did not doubt that this
figure was his father's ghost. His face was so
pale and so full of anguish that Hamlet could
not help but follow him into the shadows

of the night, where none could see or hear them.

The ghost spoke of unimagined horrors. The dead king had come to unburden his tortured soul and tell Hamlet that he had not died from a snake bite, as everyone supposed, but had been murdered – by his brother, Claudius.

"'Tis given out that, sleeping in mine orchard, a serpent stung me … but know, thou noble youth, the serpent that did sting thy father's life now wears his crown."

"O my prophetic soul! My uncle!" cried Hamlet.

Although Hamlet despised his uncle, he had not suspected him of murder.

"Oh villain, villain, smiling, damned villain!" he cried.

The ghost swore Hamlet to secrecy, but urged him to take revenge upon Claudius for his death. "If thou didst ever thy dear father love, revenge his foul and most unnatural murder!" he said.

The ghost warned Hamlet not to blame his mother, but to leave her punishment to heaven. And then he whispered, "Fare thee well. Adieu, adieu. Hamlet, remember me." With that, his father's spirit vanished like a wisp of smoke and Hamlet was alone once more.

With bitter tears, Hamlet swore by all the heavenly hosts that he would obey his father's words and revenge his foul murder. This was not a path that Hamlet would have chosen for himself, for he was a gentle prince who dreaded the thought of violence. "The time is out of joint. O cursed spite, that ever I was born to set it right," he sighed, wishing that he could be a carefree student like Horatio.

In which madness comes to Hamlet.

The days that followed were agony for Hamlet. He could not forget the anguished face of his father's ghost, nor the thought of his murder. He felt unable to trust anyone at court with the ghost's words, and the secret tore holes in his mind. Hamlet's behaviour became wild and unpredictable as he tried to hide his true thoughts. Soon everyone began to notice, including the new king's nosy chamberlain, Polonius.

"Do you know me, my lord?" Polonius
asked Hamlet.

"Excellent well; you are a fishmonger,"
replied Hamlet.

"Not I, my lord."

"Then I would you were so honest a man."

There were times when Hamlet would
exaggerate his madness, so that his uncle
Claudius and Polonius would not realize
that he suspected his father had been
murdered. There were also days when even
Hamlet could not tell if his madness was

real or contrived. He began to be cruel
to those he cared for, such as Ophelia,
Polonius's sweet daughter, whom he had
courted for many months. Hamlet's feelings
for her, which had once been so loving and
so constant, now appeared to fluctuate
between tenderness and scorn.

"I did love you once," he said, as if with no
thought for her feelings.

"Indeed my lord, you made me believe so,"
she said.

"You should not have believed me. I loved
you not," he said.

"I was the more deceived," replied
Ophelia, her heart heavy with sadness.

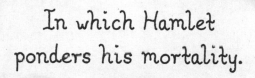

In which Hamlet
ponders his mortality.

Hamlet felt that everyone at court was
spying on him, and every day he grew more
miserable and confused. He felt he must
obey the words of his father's spirit and yet
he had no real proof that his uncle was a
murderer. Maybe his father's ghost was the
devil in disguise! He began to wonder if it
would be better to take his own life rather
than kill King Claudius. What should he do?

Should he
kill himself
or his uncle?

"To be,
or not to be:

that is the question," he said to himself.
"Whether 'tis nobler in the mind to suffer the
slings and arrows of outrageous fortune, or
to take arms against a sea of troubles, and by
opposing end them?"

Hamlet's mother, who was unaware that
Claudius had murdered her late husband,
thought Hamlet was mad with grief for his
father's death and tried to comfort him.
"Thou know'st 'tis common: all that lives
must die," she said.

Hamlet shrugged her words away. Even

if his father's death had been the only cause of his madness, he was in no mood to be comforted by his mother.

Polonius was sure that Hamlet's madness stemmed from his love for Ophelia. Only Claudius feared that there was something more sinister behind Hamlet's behaviour.

In which an awful mistake is made.

Meanwhile, Hamlet's distress grew daily as he watched his mother and his uncle together. "I am but mad north-north-west: when the wind is southerly I know a hawk from a handsaw," he told his friend Guildenstern. Yet sometimes he felt as if the wind, north-north-west or southerly, had blown all his reason away! The days and weeks passed, but still Hamlet could not bring himself to kill his uncle as the phantom had begged. For one thing, his mother and uncle were always together and he could not perform such a vile act in front of his mother. For another, he still had no real proof that his uncle was a murderer.

But then an opportunity arose to test the truth of his ghostly father's words. A famous troupe of actors arrived to perform at Elsinore Castle. Hamlet realized that he could use them to unmask King Claudius. "I'll have these players play something like the murder of my father before mine uncle:

I'll observe his looks," he decided.

On the evening of the actors' performance, the court assembled in the great hall of the castle. Torches burned and a huge fire was lit. King Claudius and his queen were in high spirits at the thought of the coming entertainment. They sat close together, whispering and laughing. No thought of her recent widowhood seemed to dull the queen's tenderness towards her new husband.

When Prince Hamlet entered with Horatio, to whom he had confided his plan, the queen beckoned to Hamlet. "Come hither, my dear Hamlet, sit by me," she smiled.

Hamlet declined and went to sit near Ophelia, whom he began to taunt and tease. When everyone was settled, the actors entered in their tattered costumes and paper crowns and the play began. On Hamlet's orders, the play mimicked the ghost's story of the murder and its consequences. Hamlet stopped taunting Ophelia and watched his uncle's face as a hawk watches his prey. Two actors walked onto the stage, dressed as a king and queen. The king lay down to sleep – and then a third actor entered and poured poison in the sleeping king's ear.

When Claudius saw this, he turned white and abruptly rose from his seat. "Give me some light: away!" he cried. He rushed

from the room with the whole court in attendance. Only Hamlet and Horatio were left behind.

"Didst perceive?" asked Hamlet. "Upon the talk of the poisoning?"

"Very well, my lord," said Horatio.

Hamlet no longer doubted his uncle's guilt. "O good Horatio! I'll take the ghost's word for a thousand pound," he said. He knew he could longer delay his revenge – he must find a way to kill his uncle.

Claudius was now certain that Hamlet suspected him of murdering his father. He asked the queen to call Hamlet to her room and find out what was on his mind. He then ordered Polonius to hide behind the wall hangings so that he could hear all that

passed between mother and son; he knew
how much Queen Gertrude loved Hamlet
and suspected that she might not tell him
everything her son said.

"Behind the arras I'll convey myself," said
Polonius, always eager to please the king.

As Polonius strutted off, King Claudius
fell to his knees. Suddenly the hideousness
of his crime seemed to overcome him.
"O! my offence is rank, it smells to heaven,"
he cried. "It hath the primal eldest curse
upon't; a brother's murder!"

As Claudius knelt in prayer with his back towards the open door, Hamlet passed by. He saw the figure of his kneeling uncle and drew his sword. He raised it high above his uncle's back, but then he hesitated. If he took his revenge now while his uncle was at prayer, Claudius's murderous soul might yet go to heaven. Better to kill him when he was not involved in some holy act. "When he is drunk asleep or in his rage, then trip him, that his soul may be as damned and black as hell, whereto it goes," muttered Hamlet, and passed on by.

Hamlet followed the dark and echoing passages of the castle until he reached his mother's room. He had been determined not to lose his temper with her, but he was unable to control his anger when Queen

Gertrude spoke of Claudius as his "father".

"Hamlet, thou hast thy father much offended," said the queen.

"Mother, you have my father much offended," replied Hamlet.

"Come, come, you answer with an idle tongue," she said.

"Go, go, you question with a wicked tongue," he retorted.

Their conversation grew more heated. In spite of his ghost father's entreaty not to blame his mother, Hamlet wanted to make her see what she had done and to repent of her wickedness. Queen Gertrude became increasingly agitated as Hamlet raged at her. She tried to run from her room, but Hamlet grabbed hold of her and pulled her back. The queen thought Hamlet was going to kill her.

"What wilt thou do? Thou wilt not murder me? Help, help, ho!" she yelled.

From his hiding place behind the tapestry, Polonius also thought that Hamlet was about to murder the queen and called out for the guards. "What, ho! Help, help, help!" he cried.

Hamlet, surprised by this faceless voice, assumed it was his uncle Claudius and plunged his sword again and again through the drapes. "How now, a rat! Dead for a ducat, dead!" he shouted.

He heard a voice gasp, "O, I am slain!"
He lifted the hanging ... and saw that he had
killed Polonius and not Claudius.

Then the ghost appeared to him once
more. It urged him to be gentler with Queen
Gertrude, but still to avenge his father's
death.

"Do you not come your tardy son to
chide?" asked Hamlet.

"Do not forget!"
replied the ghost.

Hamlet's mother,
who could neither

see nor hear the ghost, thought Hamlet was talking to himself. "Alas! He's mad," she wept.

Hamlet could hear the guard approaching. He took his leave and hurried away – dragging Polonius with him.

Hamlet hid Polonius's body and for many days refused to tell anyone where it was.

"Now, Hamlet, where's Polonius?" asked Claudius.

"At supper," replied the prince.

"At supper? Where?"

"Not where he eats, but where he is eaten," said Hamlet.

Eventually though, the old man's body was discovered and his murder gave Claudius an excuse to send Hamlet abroad. He arranged for Hamlet to sail to England in the company of his friends Rosencrantz and Guildenstern.

However, England was not far enough away for King Claudius. He would never feel safe while his nephew was still alive. He did not dare kill the young prince on Danish soil where he was known and loved, but in England Hamlet was quite unknown. There his death would cause no unpleasant ripples for Claudius. He secretly entrusted a letter to Hamlet's friends, asking the English king to execute Hamlet upon his arrival.

But on the journey to England, Hamlet found Claudius's letter. He could not forgive his friends for betraying him, so he forged a new letter, asking the king to kill Rosencrantz and Guildenstern instead of

him, and exchanged it for his uncle's note.

The ink was hardly dry when their
ship was attacked by pirates. Hamlet leapt
aboard the pirate ship to do battle with the

rogues, while his cowardly companions
deserted him and fled to England – and

their deaths. And when the pirates discovered that they had Prince Hamlet on board, they did not murder him, but returned him safely to Denmark, hoping for future favours from the royal household.

In which a fencing match goes horribly wrong.

When Hamlet reached Elsinore, he was
greeted by the news of Ophelia's death.
Her heart had been so battered by Hamlet's
strange behaviour and her father's violent
end that she had become quite deranged. She
would wander the castle grounds singing
strange and mournful songs and weaving
garlands of wild flowers. One day, while
garlanding a willow tree, she fell into the

brook below and drowned. Hamlet, for all his professed madness, had loved her dearly and he was devastated by her death – as was her brother, Laertes, who blamed Hamlet for both Ophelia's death and his father's.

Laertes hated Hamlet almost as much as King Claudius did. So when Claudius suggested that they should kill Hamlet and

make his death look like an accident, Laertes was eager to help. The plan had to be a cunning one to deceive the queen, so they sent a messenger to the prince with an invitation to a friendly fencing match. The messenger said the king had laid a bet that

Hamlet would beat
Laertes.

"I will win for
him if I can; if not, I will gain nothing but
my shame and the odd hits," replied Hamlet,
who had not for one moment forgotten his
promise to the ghost.

The court gathered to witness the battle
between Laertes and Hamlet. Laertes
made much of choosing his sword, which,
unknown to Hamlet, was not a blunt foil like
his, but needle-sharp and poisoned. Even a
small scratch would bring certain death.

Laertes and Hamlet were well matched
and both were elegant fencers. They lunged
and parried, their swords clashed, and
Hamlet scored several hits. It seemed to all,

except the king, that Hamlet would be the winner. But then Laertes suddenly lunged forward. His sword struck Hamlet's arm and drew blood.

Hamlet, realizing that Laertes was fighting with a sharpened blade, let fly his fury. He leapt at Laertes – and in the ensuing scuffle, the swords changed hands and Laertes too was wounded by his own deadly weapon.

"They bleed on both sides," Horatio shouted in horror.

Just at that moment, the queen cried out
and collapsed to the floor.

"She swoons to see them bleed," said the
king.

"No, no, the drink, the drink. O, my dear
Hamlet!" cried the queen. "The drink, the
drink; I am poison'd!"

Unwittingly, Queen Gertrude had
drunk from a poisoned cup. Hamlet at
once suspected his treacherous uncle,

and he was right to – the cup had been
prepared for him by Claudius, just in case
Laertes failed to kill him.

"O villainy! Ho! Let the door be
lock'd. Treachery, seek it out!" cried
Hamlet.

"It is here, Hamlet," said Laertes, as he too fell dying to the ground.

Laertes warned Hamlet that his wound was also mortal, for the sword had been poisoned. Then he confessed his part in Claudius's plot. "The treacherous instrument is in thy hand. Thy mother's poison'd. I can no more. The king, the king's to blame," cried Laertes – and with that, he died.

Hamlet's reaction to his uncle's fresh villainy was both sudden and violent. He leapt on Claudius and, at long last,

stabbed him with the lethal sword.

"The point envenom'd too? Then, venom, to thy work!" he cried.

Then, to make quite sure of his uncle's death, Hamlet forced him to drink from the cup of poison, saying, "Here, thou incestuous, murderous, damned Dane, drink off this potion!"

Hamlet had avenged his father's murder and his mother's murder, too. He staggered and fell to the ground calling out to his dear friend, Horatio. "I am dead, Horatio.

Wretched queen, adieu!"

Horatio ran to Hamlet and held him in his arms. As death drew near, Hamlet saw Horatio reach for the poisoned cup. "Here's yet some liquor left," he said.

Horatio wished to join his friend in death, and would have drunk the last remaining drops of poison, but Hamlet just had the strength to stay his hand.

With his dying breath, Hamlet persuaded Horatio that he must live. "Give me the cup and in this harsh world draw thy breath in pain, to tell my story," he said.

"Goodnight, sweet prince. And flights of angels sing thee to thy rest," said Horatio as his noble friend slipped away. Moments after Hamlet's death, the Prince of Norway arrived on this terrible scene of murder and revenge. After hearing the true version of events from Horatio, the Prince of Norway ordered his cannons to fire a salute. For everyone who heard the tale knew that, had the fates allowed, Hamlet, Prince of Denmark, would have been a most royal and noble king.

WILLIAM SHAKESPEARE was a popular playwright, poet and actor who lived in Elizabethan England. He married in Stratford-upon-Avon aged eighteen and had three children, although one died in childhood. Shakespeare then moved to London, where he wrote 39 plays and over 150 sonnets, many of which are still very popular today. In fact, his plays are performed more often than those of any other playwright, and he died 450 years ago! His gravestone includes a curse against interfering with his burial place, possibly to deter people from opening it in search of unpublished manuscripts. It reads, "Blessed be the man that spares these stones, and cursed be he that moves my bones." Spooky!

MARCIA WILLIAMS' mother was a novelist and her father a playwright, so it's not surprising that Marcia ended up an author herself. Although she never trained formally as an artist, she found that motherhood, and the time she spent later as a nursery school teacher, inspired her to start writing and illustrating children's books.

Marcia's books bring to life some of the world's all-time favourite stories and some colourful historical characters. Her hilarious retellings and clever observations will have children laughing out loud and coming back for more!

More retellings from Marcia Williams

ISBN 978-1-4063-5692-2

ISBN 978-1-4063-5693-9

ISBN 978-1-4063-5694-6

ISBN 978-1-4063-5695-3

Available from all good booksellers

www.walker.co.uk